Published in the UK by
POWERFRESH Limited
Unit 3 Everdon Park
Heartlands Business Park
Daventry
NN11 8YJ

Telephone  01327 871 777
Facsimile   01327 879 222
E Mail  info@powerfresh.co.uk

ISBN  1902929144

Printed in the UK by Belmont Press

# FUN & GAMES FOR THE ELDERLY

## The Silvey-Jex Partnership

THE RUDE AWAKENING

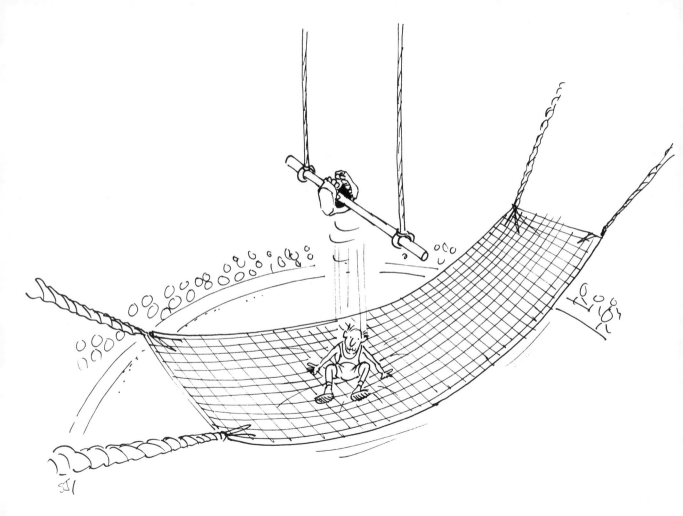

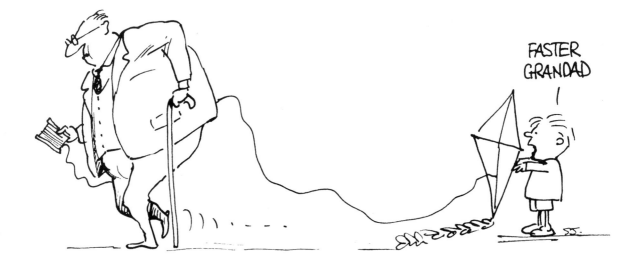

# other POWERFRESH titles

**POWERFRESH TONI GOFFE TITLES**

| | | |
|---|---|---|
| 1902929411 | FINISHED AT 50 | 2.99 : |
| 1902929403 | FARTING | 2.99 : |
| 190292942X | LIFE AFTER BABY | 2.99 : |

**POWERFRESH FUNNYSIDE SERIES**

| | | |
|---|---|---|
| 1874125260 | FUNNY SIDE OF 30 | 2.99 : |
| 1874125104 | FUNNY SIDE OF 40 HIM | 2.99 : |
| 1874125112 | FUNNY SIDE OF 40 HER | 2.99 : |
| 190292911X | FUNNY SIDE OF 50 HIM | 2.99 : |
| 1874125139 | FUNNY SIDE OF 50 HER | 2.99 : |
| 1874125252 | FUNNY SIDE OF 60 | 2.99 : |

**POWERFRESH OTHER A5**

| | | |
|---|---|---|
| 1874125171 | "CRINKLED "N" WRINKLED" | 2.99 : |
| 1874125376 | A MOTHER NO FUN | 2.99 : |
| 1874125449 | WE'RE GETTING MARRIED | 2.99 : |
| 1874125481 | CAT CRAZY | 2.99 : |
| 190292908X | EVERYTHING MEN KNOW ABOUT SEX | 2.99 : |
| 1902929071 | EVERYTHING MEN KNOW ABOUT WMN | 2.99 : |
| 1902929004 | KISSING COURSE | 2.99 : |
| 1874125996 | CONGRATULATIONS YOU'VE PASSED | 2.99 : |
| 1902929276 | TOILET VISITORS BOOK | 2.99 : |
| 1902929160 | BIG FAT SLEEPY CAT | 2.99 : |

**POWERFRESH SILVEY JEX TITLES**

| | | |
|---|---|---|
| 1902929055 | FART ATTACK | 2.99 : |
| 1874125961 | LOVE & PASSION 4 THE ELDERLY | 2.99 : |
| 187412597X | A BABY BOOK | 2.99 : |
| 1874125988 | SHEEP 'N' NASTY | 2.99 : |
| 1902929144 | FUN & FROLICS FOR THE ELDERLY | 2.99 : |
| 1902929756 | IT'S A FUNNY OLD WORLD | 3.99 : |
| 1904967108 | WRINKLIES RULE OK! | 3.99 : |
| 9781904967033 | SMILES SMIRKS & SMUT | 3.99 : |
| 9781904967507 | GOLDEN OLDUN'S | 3.99 : |
| 9781904967552 | GOLF GRATES | 3.99 : |

**POWERFRESH HUMOUR**

| | | |
|---|---|---|
| 1874125945 | GUIDE TO SEX & SEDUCTION | 3.99 : |
| 1874125848 | DICK'S NAUGHTY BOOK | 3.99 : |
| 190292925X | MODERN BABES LB OF SPELLS | 4.99 : |
| 1902929268 | A MUMS LB OF SPELLS | 4.99 : |
| 1904967000 | NOT THE OXFORD DICTIONARY | 4.99 : |
| 1904967019 | PESSIMISIMO | 4.99 : |

| | | |
|---|---|---|
| 1904967027 | POLITICAL BOLLOCKS | 4.99 : |
| 190496706X | POLITICALLY INCORRECT NOTICEBRD | 3.99 : |
| 1904967124 | JIM CRAIG ON GOLF | 3.99 : |
| 1904967132 | JIM CRAIG ON COFFEE | 3.99 : |
| 9781904967293 | KITTY CAPERS | 3.99 : |
| 9781904967286 | IT'S GONNA BE A LONG NIGHT | 4.99 : |
| 9781904967323 | GONE TO TEE | 3.99 : |

**POWERFRESH LITTLE SQUARE TITLES**

| | | |
|---|---|---|
| 1902929330 | LS DIRTY JOKES | 2.99 : |
| 1902929314 | LS DRINKING JOKES | 2.99 : |
| 1902929322 | LS GOLF JOKES | 2.99 : |
| 190292939X | LS IRISH JOKES | 2.99 : |
| 9781904967651 | LS SEXY JOKES | 2.99 : |
| 1902929292 | LS TURNING 18 | 2.99 : |
| 1902929977 | LS TURNING 21 | 2.99 : |
| 1902929969 | LS THE BIG 30 | 2.99 : |
| 1902929241 | LS THE BIG 40 | 2.99 : |
| 1902929233 | LS THE BIG 50 | 2.99 : |
| 1902929284 | LS THE BIG 60 | 2.99 : |
| 190292973X | LS DO YOU COME HERE OFTEN | 2.99 : |
| 1902929217 | LS YES BUT...! | 2.99 : |
| 1902929306 | LS WHISKY | 2.99 : |
| 1902929500 | LS HOW TO PULL BY MAGIC | 2.99 : |
| 1904967051 | LS PUB GAMES | 2.99 : |
| 1902929748 | LS SEX SLANG | 2.99 : |
| 9781904967514 | LS BE HAPPY GET LAID | 2.99 : |
| 9781904967521 | LS HT AMAZE YOUR BOSS | 2.99 : |
| 9781904967538 | LS HT AMAZE YOUR PARTNER | 2.99 : |
| 9781904967545 | LS LOSERS DON'T GET LAID | 2.99 : |
| 9781904967606 | LS WOMEN ARE LIKE | 2.99 : |
| 9781904967590 | LS MEN ARE LIKE | 2.99 : |
| 9781904967583 | LS PKT BOOK OF INSULTS | 2.99 : |
| 9781904967576 | LS THE AFFLUENCE OF INCAHOL | 2.99 : |
| 9781904967620 | LS MEN CAUTION | 2.99 : |
| 9781904967637 | LS WOMEN CAUTION | 2.99 : |
| 9781904967644 | LS HT BE A LOUSY LOVER | 2.99 : |
| 9781904967613 | LS SLIM GIRLS SECRETS | 2.99 : |
| 9781904967460 | LS 100 WAYS SEX | 2.99 : |
| 9781904967477 | LS 100 WAYS LOVER | 2.99 : |
| 9781904967484 | LS 100 WAYS LOVE LIFE | 2.99 : |
| 9781904967491 | LS 100 WAYS LOVE YOU | 2.99 : |

**POWERFRESH STATIONARY TITLES**

| | | |
|---|---|---|
| 1902929381 | WEDDING GUEST BOOK | 9.99 : |

| | | |
|---|---|---|
| 1904967094 | WEDDING PLANNER | 9.99 : |
| 1902929519 | HUMDINGER TELEPHONE BOOK | 4.99 : |
| 1902929527 | HUMDINGER ADDRESS BOOK | 4.99 : |
| 1902929535 | HUMDINGER NOTEBOOK | 2.99 : |
| 1902929810 | MODERN BABES ADDRESS BOOK | 4.99 : |
| 1902929802 | MODERN BABES TELEPHONE BOOK | 4.99 : |
| 1902929829 | MODERN BABES BIRTHDAY BOOK | 4.99 : |
| 1904967043 | GARDENERS YEAR BOOK | 4.99 : |
| 9781904967330 | BRAG BOOK FAMILY | 3.50 : |
| 9781904967347 | BRAG BOOK GRANDMA'S | 3.50 : |
| 9781904967354 | BRAG BOOK OUR BABY | 3.50 : |
| 9781904967361 | BRAG BOOK WEDDING | 3.50 : |

**POWERFRESH MINTS**

| | | |
|---|---|---|
| 5060133070009 | 18TH BIRTHDAY MINTS | 1.99 : |
| 5060133070016 | 21ST BIRTHDAY MINTS | 1.99 : |
| 5060133070023 | 30TH BIRTHDAY MINTS | 1.99 : |
| 5060133070030 | 40TH BIRTHDAY MINTS | 1.99 : |
| 5060133070047 | 50TH BIRTHDAY MINTS | 1.99 : |
| 5060133070054 | 60TH BIRTHDAY MINTS | 1.99 : |

Name _____

Address _____
_____
_____
_____

P&P £1.00 Per Parcel
Please send cheques payable to Powerfresh LTD
To Powerfresh LTD
Unit 3 Everdon Park
Heartlands Business Park
Daventry NN11 8YJ